Lift Him Up

A Songbook for Today's Christians

Compiled and Arranged by DON MARSH

B1377502

—⁕— *Songs to* —⁕—
Unite • Sing • Invite • Rejoice • Adore
Share • Praise • Surrender • Trust
Exalt • Whisper • Worship • Consecrate

The
Benson
Company

365 Great Circle Road/Nashville, Tennessee 37228

Index

Lift
Him Up

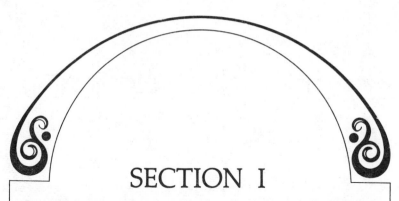

SECTION I

We Lift Our Voices In Praise And Adoration

Lift Him Up!

Words & Music by
Reba Rambo Gardner

Heavenly Father, I Appreciate You

Traditional
Arr. Don Marsh

1. Heav'n-ly Fa - ther, I ap - pre - ci - ate You. _____ Heav'n-ly
2. Son of God ___ I ___ mag - ni - fy You. _____ Son of
3. Ho - ly Spir - it, You're a com - fort to me. _____ Ho - ly
4. Tri - une God, ___ I ___ mag - ni - fy You. _____ Tri - une

Fa - ther, I ap - pre - ci - ate You. _____ I
God ___ I ___ mag - ni - fy You. _____ I
Spir - it, You're a com - fort to me. _____ I
God, ___ I ___ mag - ni - fy You. _____ I

love You, a - dore You, I bow down be -
love You, a - dore You, I bow down be -
love You, a - dore You, I bow down be -
love You, a - dore You, I bow down be -

fore You, Heav'n-ly Fa - ther, I ap - pre - ci - ate You. _____
fore You, Son of God, ___ I ___ mag - ni - fy You. _____
fore You, Ho - ly Spir - it You're a com - fort to me. _____
fore You, Tri - une God, ___ I ___ mag - ni - fy You. _____

3

Here We Are Together Again

Words & Music by
Lanny Wolfe

Here we are __ to-geth-er a-gain __ just prais-in' the Lord; __

__ Here we are __ to-geth-er a-gain __ just prais-in' the Lord. __

__ It's been a-while __ since we've seen each oth-er, __

I'm glad to be __ with my sis-ters and broth-ers; Here we are __ to-

geth-er a-gain __ just prais-in' the name __ of the Lord!

Let's Sing A Song About Jesus

Words & Music by
Lanny Wolfe

5

Mens Choir '93

This Is The Time I Must Sing

Words by William J. & Gloria Gaither

Music by William J. Gaither

1. I have tast-ed of free-dom, I can go where He's lead-ing, for
2. There are days filled with sor-row, and plans for to-mor-row, but
3. If the rocks would cry out should His prais-es die out, then the

shack-les can hold me no more. _____ I have learned of life's es-sence and I
this is the time I must sing. _____ And I know there's a rea-son why.
stones must keep si-lent as long. _____ As I've breath for the sing-ing His

stand in His pres-ence and sing with my heart, "He is Lord." _____
in His own sea-son God gives me a song I can sing. _____ Keep
praise will keep ring-ing, and I will keep sing-ing my song. _____

Chorus

si-lent ye moun-tains, ye fields and ye foun-tains for this is the

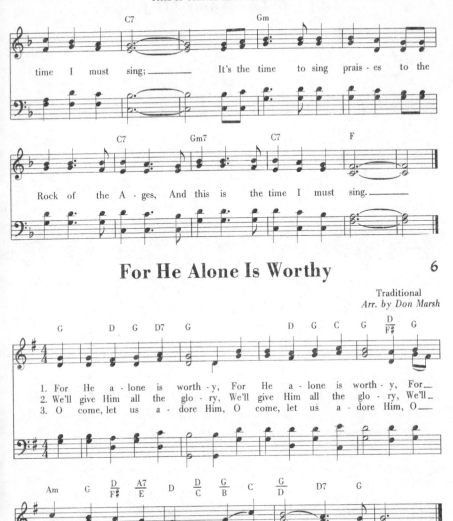

time I must sing;_____ It's the time to sing prais-es to the
Rock of the A-ges, And this is the time I must sing._____

For He Alone Is Worthy

6

Traditional
Arr. by Don Marsh

1. For He a-lone is worth-y, For He a-lone is worth-y, For__ He__ a-lone is worth-y,_____
2. We'll give Him all the glo-ry, We'll give Him all the glo-ry, We'll give__ Him all the glo-ry,_____ Christ_____ the Lord!
3. O come, let us a-dore Him, O come, let us a-dore Him, O__ come, let us a-dore__ Him,__

Lift Up The Name Of Jesus

Words & Music by
Phil Johnson

I Want To Thank You, Jesus

Words & Music by
Jane & Don Marsh

I want to thank You, Je - sus, I want to thank You, Je - sus, I want to thank You, Je - sus, I want to give you the praise! You gave Your life to save me, and now You live with - in me. I want to thank You, Je - sus, for all You mean to me.

9

Jesus, You Have Been Good To Me

Words & Music by
Terry Harper

Je - sus, You have been good___ to me,___

Je - sus, You have been good___ to me,___ Je-sus, You have been good___

___ to me,___ Oh praise Your name!___

10

Song Of Love

Words & Music by
Dallas Holm

1. Je - sus, Je - sus, Je - sus,
2. Love___ Him, Love___ Him, Love___ Him,
* 3. Praise___ Him, Praise___ Him, Praise___ Him,

Worth-y is the Lamb, Oh _ Glo-ry to the name of _ Je - sus! _

Other verses - Worship Him, Serve Him, Follow Him

Doxology

11

Words by Thomas Ken

Music by Louis Bourgeois

Praise God, from whom all bless -ings flow. Praise Him all crea - tures

here be - low; Praise Him a - bove, Ye heav'n-ly host. Praise

Fa - ther, Son and Ho - ly _ Ghost! A - men.

Bless That Wonderful Name

Words & Music partially traditional and
by Rick Powell

Moderately fast

Chorus: Bless that won-der-ful Name.
1. free-dom in __ that Name. of __ Je - sus, _____
2. pow-er in __ that Name.

Bless that won-der-ful Name.
free-dom in __ that Name. of __ Je - sus. _____
pow-er in __ that Name.

Bless that won-der-ful Name.
free-dom in __ that Name. of __ Je - sus, _____
pow-er in __ that Name.

Last time to Coda |1, 2, 3

No oth-er Name __ I know. _____ *To Chorus*
1. There's __
2.
3. There's __

BLESS THAT WONDERFUL NAME

know._____ There's love_ (there is love__) and pow- er,_____

There's grace_ (there is grace__) and com - fort;_____ There's

pow'r (there is pow'r_) and glo - ry._____ He's wait-ing now for

you to call;_ Call on Je - sus._ Oh,

know._____

D.S. al ⊕ Coda
(to Coda)

⊕ Coda

Come On, Let's Praise Him

Words & Music by
Lanny Wolfe

COME ON, LET'S PRAISE HIM

1. Praise ye the Lord ____ Praise His ho - ly name, __
2. Come on let's praise _ Him, Let the heav - en's ring, __

Praise _ ye the Lord, __ Let the world pro - claim; _
Make a joy - ful noise, __ Clap your hands and sing; __

He is King and Lord of all, ____ Bow be - fore Him great and small, _
Worlds were formed at His com-mand, _ He holds all pow - er in His hand, _

Let ev - 'ry - thing _ praise the King of Kings, _ praise the King of Kings! _

All My Praise

14

Words & Music by
Terry Harper

1. I re-mem-ber the night when I found the
2. How can I thank You for Your love to me,

Lord, And the warmth of His love I felt; Then I gave Him con-
For the joy You have brought my way; I'm un-wor-thy of

trol and my heart o-ver-flowed, as on my knees I knelt.
You, but what else can I do, Ex-cept to kneel and pray?

Chorus

All my praise I give Thee, Lord, As I hum-bly come to Thee;

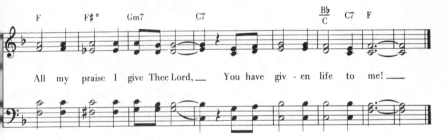

All my praise I give Thee Lord, ___ You have giv-en life to me! ___

Glory Be To The Father

15

Gloria Patria

Traditional

Music by Henry W. Greatorex

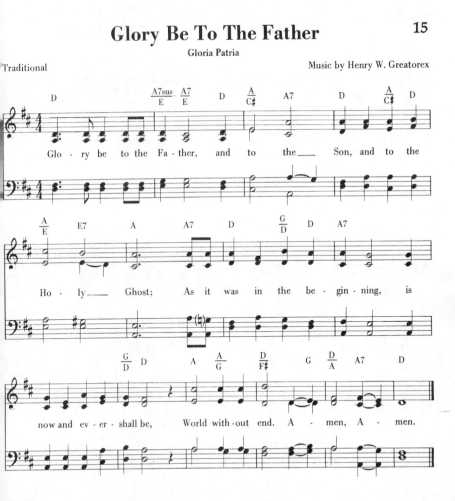

Glo - ry be to the Fa - ther, and to the ___ Son, and to the

Ho - ly ___ Ghost; As it was in the be - gin - ning, is

now and ev - er - shall be, World with-out end. A - men, A - men.

Blessed Be The Name

Adapted from Charles Wesley

R.E. Hudson

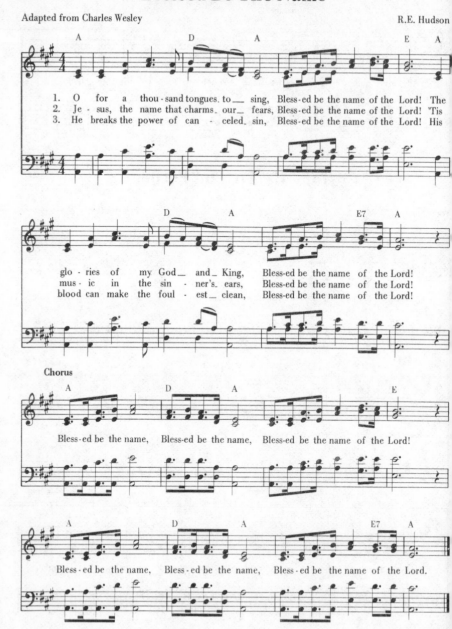

1. O for a thou-sand tongues to sing, Bless-ed be the name of the Lord! The
2. Je - sus, the name that charms our fears, Bless-ed be the name of the Lord! 'Tis
3. He breaks the power of can - celed sin, Bless-ed be the name of the Lord! His

glo - ries of my God and King, Bless-ed be the name of the Lord!
mus - ic in the sin - ner's ears, Bless-ed be the name of the Lord!
blood can make the foul - est clean, Bless-ed be the name of the Lord!

Chorus

Bless-ed be the name, Bless-ed be the name, Bless-ed be the name of the Lord!

Bless - ed be the name, Bless - ed be the name, Bless - ed be the name of the Lord.

Bless His Holy Name

Words & Music by
Andrae Crouch

Praise Be To Jesus

18

Words by Gloria Gaither

Music by William J. Gaither

Praise be to Je-sus, the sweet Rose of Shar-on. Praise to the

Christ, the Re-deem-er of men; Praise to the King who is

reign-ing for-ev-er, The Hope of the a-ges, My Mas-ter and Friend.

Praises

19

Words & Music by
W. Elmo Mercer

Prais - es, I'll sing prais - es _____ to the One who gave His

life that I might live;＿＿＿ Prais - es, I'll sing

prais - es＿＿＿ to Je - sus, my Re-deem - er, my Friend.＿＿＿

He Is Lord 20

Traditional
Arr. by Don Marsh

He is Lord, He is Lord; He is ris - en from the dead and He is

Lord. Ev - 'ry knee shall bow, ev - 'ry tongue con - fess that Je - sus Christ is Lord!

My Tribute

Words & Music by
Andrae Crouch

To God be the glo - ry, to God be the glo - ry, To

God be the glo - ry, for the things He has done! With His

blood He has saved me, With His pow'r He has raised me; To

God be the glo - ry, For the things— He has done! done. Just let me

MY TRIBUTE

live my life, Let it be pleas-ing Lord, to Thee; And if I

gain an-y praise, Let it go to Cal - va - ry! With His

O For A Thousand Tongues

22

Charles Wesley

Carl G. Glaser

1. O for a thou-sand tongues to sing My great Re-deem-er's praise,
2. My gra-cious Mas-ter and my God, As-sist me to pro-claim,
3. Je-sus! the name that charms our fears, That bids our sor-rows cease;
4. He breaks the power of can-celed sin, He sets the pris-oner free;

The glo-ries of my God and King, The_ tri-umphs of His grace.
To spread through all the earth a-broad The_ hon-ors of Thy name.
'Tis mu-sic in the sin-ner's ears, 'Tis_ life, and health, and peace.
His blood can make the foul-est clean; His_ blood a-vailed for me.

Sometimes Alleluia

Words & Music by
Chuck Girard

23

Chorus

Some-times, "Al - le -lu - ia," some-times, "Praise the Lord," __

Some-times gen - tly sing - ing, Our hearts in one ac - cord. __ *Fine*

Verse

1. Oh let us lift our voic - es,
2. Oh let us feel His pres - ence,
3. Oh let our joy be un - con - fined,
4. Oh let the Spir - it o - ver - flow,

Look to-ward the sky and start to sing; ____
Let the sound of prais - es fill the air; ____
Let us sing with free - dom un - re - strained; ____
As __ we are filled from head to toe ____

Oh let us now re - turn His love, ___
Oh let us sing the song of Je - sus' ___ love,
Let's take this feel - ing that we feel ___ now,
We love You, Fa - ther, Son, and Ho - ly ___ Ghost,

Just _ let our voic - es ring! ___
To _ peo - ple, ev - 'ry - where! ___
Out _ side these walls and let it ring! ___
And we want this world ___ to know! ___

Jesus, I Feel Your Touch

24

Words & Music by
Rich Cook

Soulfully - not too fast

1. Je - sus, Je - sus,
2. Praise Him, Praise Him,

Je - sus, ___ I feel Your touch.
Praise Him, ___ I feel His touch.

* Other verses - Thank Him, Love Him, Serve Him.

25

I Will Praise Him

Mrs. M.J. Harris

I will praise Him! I will praise Him! Praise the Lamb for sin-ners slain;

Give Him glo-ry, all ye peo-ple, For His blood can wash a-way each stain.

26

Before The Rocks Cry Out

Words by Rich Cook

Music by Dave Feit

Not too fast

Chorus

Be-fore the rocks cry out, I just have to praise Him, Just have to

thank Him for all that He's done. Be-fore all na-ture ris-es

up to shout, I just have to thank Him for all He's done for me.

I Just Came To Praise The Lord 27

Words & Music by
Wayne Romero

1. I just came to praise the Lord,_____ I just came to praise the
2. I just came to thank the Lord,_____ I just came to praise the

Lord._____ I just came to praise His
Lord._____ I just came to praise His

Ho - ly_____ Name; I just came to praise_ the Lord.__
Ho - ly_____ Name; I just came to thank_ the Lord.__

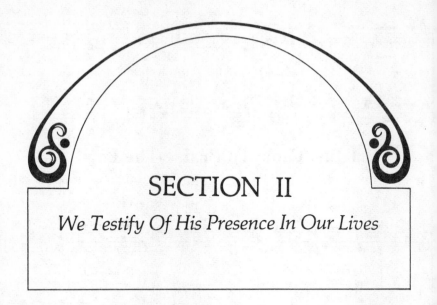

SECTION II

We Testify Of His Presence In Our Lives

28

O How I Love Jesus

Frederick Whitfield

American melody

O how I love Je - sus, O how I love Je - sus,

O how I love Je - sus, Be - cause He first loved me!

When I Say Jesus

Words & Music by
Phil Johnson

When I say "Mas-ter," My sor-rows dis-ap-pear;

When I say, "Fa-ther," He drives a-way my fears.

When I say "Sav-iour," my blind-ed eyes can see,

When I say "Je-sus," He speaks peace to me!

The Way, The Truth, The Life

Words & Music by
Anita Grund

1. Men are striv-ing to find the an-swers to the ques-tions that nev-er cease; They find in life there's some-thing miss-ing _____ They are look-ing _____ for re-lease, And the way _____ to peace. _____

2. If you're look-ing _____ for a chal-lenge, if you dare _____ give Him a try; _____ Put your life in-to His keep-ing, _____ It was for you _____ He came to die, Don't _ pass _ Him by. _____ He is the

THE WAY, THE TRUTH, THE LIFE

31 There's Something That's Different About Him

Words & Music by
Lanny Wolfe

There's some-thing that's dif-f'rent a-bout Him for His voice has calmed the an-gry rag-ing sea, There's some-thing that's dif-f'rent a-bout Him, For His touch has changed a sin-ful wretch like me, And al-though I can't ex-plain, things are dif-f'rent since He came; There's some-thing dif-f'rent a-bout the One whose name is Je-sus!

There's Just Something About My Jesus

Words & Music by
Terry Harper

32

A Wonderful Feeling

Words & Music by
Lanny Wolfe

Well it's a won-der-ful feel - ing when you know you've found _____ what you've been look-ing for! _____ No more search-ing, no more look-ing a-round ___ to find some-thing worth liv-ing for. _____ I found Je - sus and there's no doubt a-bout ___ it, He's ev-'ry-thing I want - ed and more, ___

A WONDERFUL FEELING

And it's a won-der-ful feel - ing when you

know you've found _____ what you've been look-ing for! _____

Love Lifted Me

34

James Rowe

Howard E. Smith

Love lift - ed me, _____ Love lift - ed me, _____ When noth - ing
e - ven me, e - ven me,

else could help, Love lift - ed me; _____ Love lift - ed me. _____

Ever Gentle, Ever Sweet

Words & Music by
Stephen Adams

1. His love is like a roll-in' riv-er, a clear and cool re-treat, Flow-ing on in calm and beau-ty,
2. His love is like an A-pril show-er with a stead-y beat, Sprink-ling drops of joy and beau-ty, Gen-tle, ev-er sweet!
3. His love is like a wind that's whis-p'rin' soft-ly through the wheat, Scat-ter-ing, the seeds of beau-ty,

Chorus

Ev-er gen-tle ev-er sweet, Gen-tle, ev-er sweet. His love is like a roll-in' river,
love is like an A-pril show-er, Gen-tle, ev-er sweet.
a wind that's whis-p'rin',

I Live

Words & Music by
Rich Cook

Blessed Assurance

Fanny J. Crosby

Phoebe P. Knapp

Sav - iour all the day long; _____ This is my sto - ry, this is my song, _____ Prais - ing my Sav - iour all the day long. _____

Jesus Paid It All

38

Mrs. H. M. Hall

John T. Grape

Je - sus paid it all, All to Him I owe; Sin had left a crim - son stain, He washed it white as snow.

God Said It, I Believe It, That Settles It

Words by Stephen Adams and Gene Braun

Music by Stephen Adams

1. "Faith is the es-sence of things un-seen____ the sub-stance of things hoped for." God's Word has said it, and I be-lieve it for the mir-a-cle has hap-pened to me!

2. God is the Au-thor and He's the end-ing____ of all that I be-lieve in, Life more a-bun-dant is yours for the ask-ing for the mir-a-cle can hap-pen to you!

Chorus

God said it, and I be-lieve it, and that set-tles it for me! God said it, and I be-

GOD SAID IT . . . I BELIEVE IT . . . THAT SETTLES IT

lieve it, and that set-tles it for me! Though some may doubt that His

Word is true, I've cho-sen to be-lieve it, now how a-bout you? God

said it, and I be-lieve it, and that set-tles it for me!

40

My Savior's Love

Chas. H. Gabriel

How mar-vel-ous! how won-der-ful! And my song shall ev-er be
Oh, how mar-vel-ous! oh, how won-der-ful!

How mar-vel-ous! how won-der-ful Is my Sav-ior's love for me!
Oh, how mar-vel-ous! oh, how won-der-ful

Jesus Got Ahold O' My Life

Words & Music by
Dallas Holm

Je-sus got a-hold o' my life __ and He won't let me go. __

Je-sus got in - to my heart _ He got in - to my soul. __ I

used to be __ oh so sad, _ But now I'm just a free and glad, _ 'Cause

Je-sus got a-hold o' my life __ and He won't let me go. __

JESUS GOT AHOLD O' MY LIFE

Jesus Did It For Me

Words & Music by
Lanny Wolfe

1. You ask me how I know Je-sus blood wash-es
2. I know with-out a doubt Je-sus love can

whit-er than snow, I can say that I know it's so be-cause, Je-sus did it for me!
bring you out, And give you some-thing to sing a-bout be-cause,

Take a life that's been bro-ken by sin, Je-sus blood can
He'll make your path-way bright, And take a-way all your

mend it a-gain Give you joy that will nev-er end be-cause
sin and strife And write your name in the Book of Life be-cause

JESUS DID IT FOR ME

Chorus

Tears Are A Language
(God Understands)

43

Words & Music by
Gordon Jensen

1. Oft - en you've won - dered why ___ tears come in - to your eyes,
2. When grief has left you low, ___ it caus - es tears to flow,

And bur - dens seem to be much more than you can stand.
Things have not turned out the way that you had planned.

But God is ___ stand - ing near, ___ He sees your
But God won't for - get ___ you, ___ His prom - is -

fall - ing tears, Tears are ___ a lan - guage, God un - der - stands.
es are true,

TEARS ARE A LANGUAGE

Chorus

God sees the tears of a bro-ken heart-ed soul, ____ He sees your tears and hears them when they fall. ____ God weeps a-long with man ___ and takes him by the hand; __ Tears are _ a lan-guage, God un-der-stands. ____

Amazing Grace

John Newton

Traditional
Arr. by Don Marsh

1. A- maz- ing grace! How sweet the sound, That saved a wretch like me! I once was lost but now am found, Was blind but now I see.

2. 'Twas grace that taught my heart to fear, And grace my fears relieved; How precious did that grace appear, The hour I first believed!

3. Through man- y dan- gers, toils and snares, I have al- read- y come; 'Tis grace hath brought me safe thus far, And grace will lead me home.

4. When we've been there ten thou- sand years, Bright shin- ing as the sun; We've no less days to sing God's praise Than when we first begun.

I Just Love Lovin' The Lord

Words & Music by
Rich Cook

I just love lovin' the Lord— more than an-y-thing else—that I do,—

I just love lovin' the Lord— I love prais-in' and serv-in' Him too. Some

folks love mu-sic that's why they sing,—But that a-lone my friend is not e-nough for—me—be-cause I

just love lovin' the Lord— more than an-y -thing else—that I do.——

I Just Feel Like Something Good
Is About To Happen

Words & Music by
William J. Gaither

1. I just feel like some-thing good is a-bout to hap - pen,
2. I have learned in all that hap - pens_ just to praise Him,
3. Yes I've no - ticed all the bad news_ in the pa - per,

I just feel like some-thing good is on _ its way;
For I know He's work - ing all things for_ my good;
And it seems like things are bleak - er ev - 'ry day;

He has prom - ised that He'd o - pen all of Heav - en,
Ev - 'ry tear I shed is worth all the in - vest - ment,
℣ But for this child of God it makes no dif - f'rence,

℣ And broth - er, it ___ could hap - pen an - y day.
For I know He'll see_ me through, He said He would.
℣ Be - cause it's bound to get bet - ter ei - ther way.

I JUST FEEL LIKE SOMETHING GOOD IS ABOUT TO HAPPEN

A Broken Heart I Gave

Words & Music by
Russ Lindberg

1. One day I lost my way___ but no one cared,
2. Have you been won-der-ing___ why you're a-lone?

___ I searched for hap-pi-ness___ but found des-pair; ___ Then Je-sus
___ Does God seem far a-way___ you doubt His love? ___ Now Christ is

spoke to me___ re-vealed to me my sin, "I'll heal your
at the door___ He sees a heart that's torn, His blood was

Chorus

bro-ken heart if I may en-ter in."___ A bro-ken
shed for you to give you life a-new.___

A BROKEN HEART I GAVE

heart I gave, a worth-less thing. _____ An emp-ty life was all _____ that I could bring; _____ Then Je-sus filled my life _____ with love di-vine, _____ He healed my bro-ken heart and now I know He's mine. _____

Worthy

48

Rich Cook

1. Worth - y, Worth - y, Worth - y is the Lamb!
2. Glo - ry, Glo - ry, Glo - ry to His name!
3. Ho - ly, Ho - ly, Ho - ly is the Lord!
4. Praise Him. Praise Him, Praise Him, ev - er - more!
5. Je - sus, Je - sus, Je - sus, is my Lord!
6. Thank Him, Thank Him, Thank Him, ev - er - more!

Worth - y is the Lamb!
Glo - ry to His name!
Ho - ly is the Lord!
Praise Him ev - er - more!
Je - sus, is my Lord!
Thank Him ev - er - more!

Only Jesus Can Satisfy Your Soul

49 √

Words & Music by
Lanny Wolfe

1. The world will try to sat-is-fy ___ that long-ing in your soul. You may search the wide world o'er ___ but you'll be just as be-fore. You'll never find true sat-is-fac-tion un-til you've found the Lord, for on-ly Je-sus ___ can sat-is-fy your soul. ___ On-ly

2. If you could have the fame and for-tune, all the wealth you could ob-tain. Yet you have not Christ with-in, your liv-ing here would be in vain. There'll come a time when death shall call you, rich-es can-not help you then, so come to Je-sus ___ for on-ly He can sat-is-fy. ___

ONLY JESUS CAN SATISFY YOUR SOUL

Chorus

Je - sus can sat - is - fy your soul; _____ And on - ly He _____ can change your heart _____ and make you whole. _____ He'll give you peace _____ you nev - er knew, Sweet love and joy, _____ and Heav - en too; For on - ly Je - sus can sat - is - fy your soul! _____

50 ✓

Jesus
(He is the Son of God)

Words & Music by
Danny Lee

1. The busy streets and sidewalks, they suddenly grew still, As a Man came through the entrance of the city. As He touched and healed the blind man with a little piece of
2. There are footprints in the sand along the sea of Galilee, Where thousands came to hear and came to see Him. There He taught of love and kindness yes He brought a better
3. Then the air grew cold and the sky turned black as they nailed Him to a tree, There He died for ev'ry man and ev'ry country. But the price He paid and the blood He shed is changing lives to-

JESUS (HE IS THE SON OF GOD)

clay, With _ trem-bling lips you could hear the peo-ple say._____
way, As He spoke they'd turn and___ whis-per and they'd say._____
day, And with joy and praise you can hear these peo-ple say._____

Chorus

Je - sus, Je - sus, He is the Son of God. Je - sus,

Je - sus, the pre - cious Son of God.___ Sweet - est Rose of

Shar - on came to set us free; Je - sus, Je - sus, He's

ev - 'ry-thing to me; Yes, He's all the world to me._____

I Have Something To Sing About

Words & Music by
Stephen Adams

I____ have some-thing to sing a-bout.____

I've found some-thing and that some-thing is a some-one,

And since I've found Him I've found that I can't live with-out Him,

If I failed ___ to praise the Lord ___ the

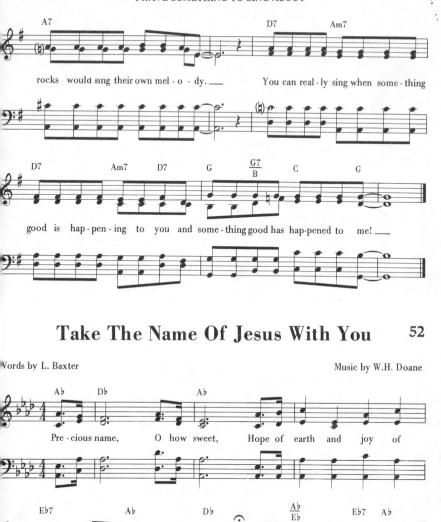

rocks would sing their own mel - o - dy. ___ You can real - ly sing when some - thing

good is hap - pen - ing to you and some - thing good has hap-pened to me! ___

Take The Name Of Jesus With You 52

Words by L. Baxter

Music by W.H. Doane

Pre - cious name, O how sweet, Hope of earth and joy of

heav'n; Pre - cious name, O how sweet ___ Hope of earth and joy of heav'n.

53 It Is Well With My Soul

H.G. Spafford

P.P. Bliss

1. When peace, like a riv-er, at-tend-eth my way, When sor-rows like
2. My sin oh, the bliss of this glo-ri-ous thought—My sin—not in
3. And Lord, haste the day when the faith shall be sight, The clouds be rolled

sea bil-lows roll; What-ev-er my lot, Thou hast taught me to
part, but the whole—Is nailed to the cross and I bear it no
back as a scroll, The trump shall re-sound and the Lord shall de-

say, It is well, it is well with my soul.
more, Praise the Lord, praise the Lord, O my soul!
scend, "E-ven so"—it is well with my soul.

Chorus

It is well _____

with my soul, _____ It is well, it is well with my soul.

It is _____ well _____ with my soul.

Jesus Is Still The Answer

Words & Music by
Lanny Wolfe

Jesus, The Resurrection

Words & Music by
Rich Cook

1. Sin was my mas-ter with death as wag-es, Caught in the
2. Though I was dead I now am liv-ing, I am a-

clutch-es of guilt and shame; Then Je-sus came and
live in Je-sus' name; His death at Cal-v'ry re-

loosed my shack-les, No more sin could free-ly reign.
placed my suf-f'ring, I'm res-ur-rect-ed to sing His praise!

Chorus

Je-sus, the Res-ur-rec-tion, Je-sus, the Res-ur-rec-tion,

Je - sus, the Res - ur - rec - tion, Je - sus has giv - en me life!____

Oh, How He Loves You And Me

56

Words & Music by
Kurt Kaiser

Oh, how He loves you and me!_____ Oh, how He loves you and

me!_____ He gave His life, what_ more could He give? Oh, how He

loves you, Oh, how He loves me, Oh, how He loves you and me!_____

All In The Name Of Jesus

Words & Music by
Stephen R. Adams

1. Truth and beau-ty, __ hap - pi - ness, It's all in the
2. Care and com-fort, __ heal - ing and grace It's all in the

name of Je - sus; _____ Health and Heav - en, __
name of Je - sus; _____ Wel - come, par - don, __ a

peace and rest, It's all in the name of Je - sus. ____
hid - ing place, It's all in the name of Je - sus. ____

Joy and glad-ness, __ for - give - ness too Life __ ev - er -
Warmth and sun-shine, _____ friend ship true, Ful - fill - ment and __

ALL IN THE NAME OF JESUS

I Found It All In Jesus

Words & Music by
W. Elmo Mercer

1. While I sought for rich - es and plea - sures un - told,
2. All a - lone I had trav - eled the long road of life,

I longed for peace in my heart; _____ But when I came to Je - sus and
Seek - ing for some-one who cared; _____ When I found on - ly heart-ache and

gave Him con - trol, He gave real joy from the start! _____
trou - ble and _ strife, I prayed to God in des - pair. _____

Chorus

I found it all in Je - sus! _____ My search - ing is through, all things are

new. I found it all in Je - sus, ___ And you can find Him, too! ___

There's Life In Jesus' Name 59

Words & Music by
Rich Cook

There's life ___ in Je - sus'_ name, there's cleans - ing, there's heal-ing in

Je - sus'_ name; Be - lieve Him, come un - to Him, re - ceive from His

pow'r, ___ For in Je - sus' name, There's life for you this hour. ___

This Moment

Words & Music by
Rich Cook

Blessin' After Blessin'

Words & Music by
John Stallings

61

Greater Is He That Is In Me

Words & Music by
Lanny Wolfe

GREATER IS HE

may de - vour,__ the Bi - ble tells me so. __ Man - y souls have
up - per room__ and bap - tized all of them.__ With a pow - er

been His prey __ to fall in some weak hour, __ But
great - er than __ an - y earth - ly foe, __ And

God has prom - ised us to - day____ His__ o - ver com - ing pow'r.__
I'm so glad I've got it, too,__ I'm gon - na let the whole world know.__

Alleluia

63

(canon)

Very slowly

Come in - to His pres - ence sing - ing, "Al - le - lu - ia! Al - le - lu - ia! Al - le - lu - ia!"

The Joy Of The Lord

Words and Music by
Alliene G. Vale

64

1. The joy __ of the Lord __ is my strength, The
2. He giv - eth liv - ing wa - ter and I thirst no more, He
3. He heals the bro - ken heart - ed and they cry no more, He

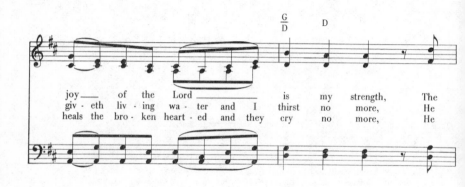

joy __ of the Lord __ is my strength, The
giv - eth liv - ing wa - ter and I thirst no more, He
heals the bro - ken heart - ed and they cry no more, He

joy __ of the Lord __ is my strength, The
giv - eth liv - ing wa - ter and I thirst no more, The
heals the bro - ken heart - ed and they cry no more, The

THE JOY OF THE LORD

joy ___ of the Lord ___ is my strength.
joy ___ of the Lord ___ is my strength.
joy ___ of the Lord ___ is my strength.

Additional verses,
4. The word of faith is nigh thee, even in Thy mouth, etc.
5. He fills my mouth with laughter and I say, "ha, ha, " etc.

Higher Ground

65

Johnson Oatman, Jr.

Charles H. Gabriel

Lord, lift me up and let me stand By faith on Heav - en's ta - ble -
land, A high-er plane than I have found; Lord, plant my feet on high - er ground.

Hey! I'm A Believer Now

Words & Music by
Dallas Holm

Trusting Jesus

E. Page

Ira D. Sankey

Trust - ing as the mo - ments fly, Trust - ing as the days go by; ___

Trust - ing Him what - e'er be - fall, Trust - ing Je - sus, that is all.

Rise Again

Words & Music by
Dallas Holm

1. Go a - head, drive the nails_ in my hands, Laugh at me where you

stand. Go a - head, and say it is - n't me, the

RISE AGAIN

RISE AGAIN

bur - y me _____ but ver - y soon _ I will _ be free, _ 'Cause I'll

ground. 3. Go a - head and say I'm dead and gone, But

you _ will see _ that you _ were wrong. _ Go a - head, try to

hide _ the Son, But all _ will see _ that I'm _ the One! _ 'Cause I'll

Each Step I Take

W.E.M.

W. Elmo Merc[...]

1. Each step I take my Savior goes be - fore me, And with His
2. At times I feel my faith be - gin to wa - ver, When up a -
3. I trust in God, no mat - ter come what may, ___ For life e -

lov - ing hand He leads the way; ___ And with each breath I whis - per, "I a -
head I see a chas - m wide; ___ It's then I turn and look up to my
ter - nal is in His hand; ___ He holds the key that o - pens up the

dore Thee!" O what joy to walk with Him each day. ___
Sav - ior, I am strong when He is by my side. ___
way ___ That will lead me to the prom - ised land. ___

Chorus

Each step I take I know that He will guide me — To high - er

ground He ev - er leads me on; ___ Un - til some day the last step will be

tak - en, Each step I take just leads me clos - er home. ___

Just A Closer Walk

70

Traditional
Arr. Don Marsh

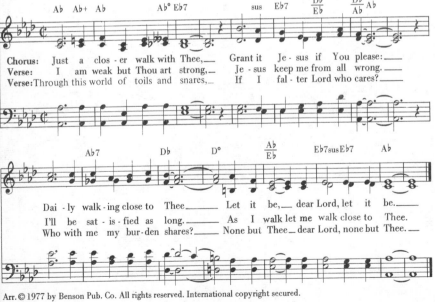

Chorus: Just a clos - er walk with Thee, ___ Grant it Je - sus if You please: ___
Verse: I am weak but Thou art strong, ___ Je - sus keep me from all wrong. ___
Verse: Through this world of toils and snares, ___ If I fal - ter Lord who cares? ___

Dai - ly walk - ing close to Thee ___ Let it be, ___ dear Lord, let it be. ___
I'll be sat - is - fied as long. ___ As I walk let me walk close to Thee.
Who with me my bur - den shares? ___ None but Thee ___ dear Lord, none but Thee. ___

We Have Overcome

Words & Music by
Tom Springer

Chorus

We have o-ver-come, We have o-ver-come; By the words of our mouth, by the blood of the Lamb, _____ We have o-ver-come.

Verse

1. Who so - ev - er is born of _____ God _____
   Hold - ing _____ fast to _____ our con - fes - sion,
2. March - ing to Zi - on, _____ beau - ti - ful cit - y,
   O - ver - com - ers _____ shall march tri - um - phant,
3. Fight out the fight fin - ish the course, _____
   Fin - 'lly my breth - ren be strong in the Lord, _____

o - ver___ com - eth the world;
of Je - sus as our___ Lord,
bat - tles___ are all___ won;
through those___ gates of___ pearl;
you must___ keep the___ faith;
and in the pow'r of His might;

Join in the vic - to - ry
We'll share His throne,___
Fol - low our Cap - tain
Wav - ing our ban - ner,
You shall in - her - it
Wear - ing the arm - or,

won by___ faith___ for we have o - ver come!
we'll rule the na - tions for we have o - ver come!
who's gone be - fore___ us for we have o - ver come!
shout - ing the vic - to - ry for we have o - ver come!
a crown of glo - ry for we have o - ver come!
stand as a con - quer - or for you have o - ver come!

Jesus Loves Me

72

Wm. Bradbury

Yes, Je - sus loves me, Yes, Je - sus loves me. Yes, Je - sus loves me, the Bi - ble tells me so!

73. No One Ever Cared For Me Like Jesus

Words & Music by
C.F. Weigle

1. I would love to tell you what I think of Je - sus, Since I found in Him a Friend so strong and true. I would tell you how He changed my life com - plete - ly, He did some - thing that no oth - er friend could do.

2. All my life was full of sin when Je - sus found me, All my heart was full of mis - er - y and woe. Je - sus placed His strong and lov - ing arms a - bout me, And He led me in the way I ought to go.

3. Ev - 'ry day He comes to me with new as - sur - ance, More and more I un - der - stand His words of love. But I'll nev - er know just why He came to save me, Till some day I see His bless - ed face a - bove. No one

Chorus — NO ONE EVER CARED FOR ME LIKE JESUS

ev - er cared for me like Je - sus, There's no

oth - er friend so kind as He; No one else could take the sin and dark-ness

from me, O how much He cared for me.

Hiding In Thee

74

Words by W. Cushing

Music by Ira Sankey

Hid - ing in Thee, Hid - ing in Thee: Thou

blest Rock of A - ges, I'm hid - ing in Thee.

We're Not Strangers Anymore

Words & Music by
Danny Lee

1. From the man-ger where He lay to the gar-den where He prayed,
2. I had heard a-bout this Man who could e-ven raise the dead,
3. If you're look-ing for a friend who'll go with you to the end,

I'd of-ten heard a-bout this stran-ger; _____ Then I o-pened up my
I heard He calmed the trou-bled wa-ters; _____ But I nev-er thought for
Some-one who's clos-er than a broth-er; _____ Why not give this man a

heart _____ and He walked in-to my life, Now we're not stran-gers an-y-
me _____ He would calm the rag-ing sea, But all I do is call His
try _____ for e-ven now He's pass-ing by, You won't be stran-gers an-y-

more.
name.
more.

Chorus

1.2 For He's my Friend, _____ He's my Lord, _____
3. He'll be your Friend, _____ and your Lord, _____

WE'RE NOT STRANGERS ANYMORE

Oh how I love Him, He's my Fa - ther;____ Now we walk____ hand in
Oh how you'll love Him as your Fa - ther;____ Then you'll walk____ hand in

hand,____ For we're not stran - gers an - y - more.____
hand,____ You won't be stran - gers an - y - more.____

'Tis So Sweet To Trust In Jesus   76

Louisa M.R. Stead   Wm. J. Kirkpatrick

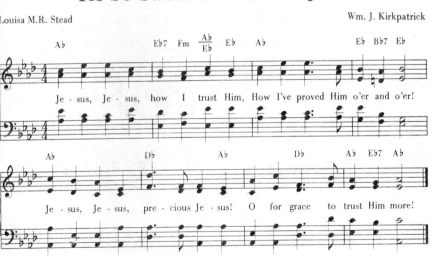

Je - sus, Je - sus, how I trust Him, How I've proved Him o'er and o'er!

Je - sus, Je - sus, pre - cious Je - sus! O for grace to trust Him more!

Quartet

I Feel Good!

Words & Music by
Lanny and Marietta Wolfe

I feel good! I feel good! Just to know I've been re-
deemed makes me feel good! I feel good! I feel good!
Just to know I've been re-deemed makes me feel good!

1. Oh how well do I re-mem-ber all the days I spent in
2. Now I'm on my way to Heav-en and I'm sing-ing as I
3. When my trav-'ling days are o-ver and I reach that hap-py

I FEEL GOOD

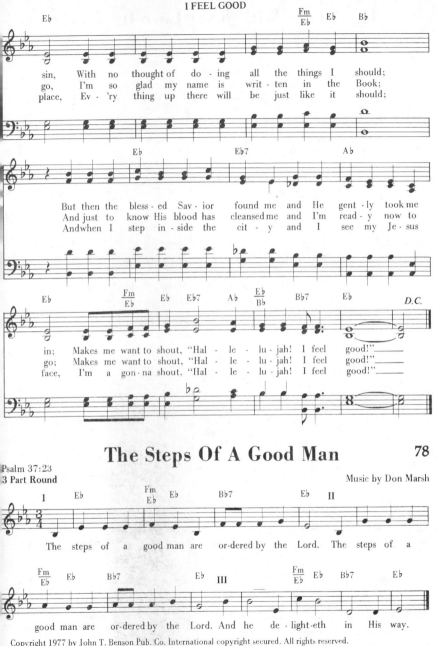

Eb · Fm/Eb · Eb · Bb

sin, With no thought of do-ing all the things I should;
go, I'm so glad my name is writ-ten in the Book;
place, Ev-'ry thing up there will be just like it should;

Eb · Eb7 · Ab

But then the bless-ed Sav-ior found me and He gent-ly took me
And just to know His blood has cleansed me and I'm read-y now to
And when I step in-side the cit-y and I see my Je-sus

Eb · Fm/Eb · Eb · Eb7 · Ab · Eb/Bb · Bb7 · Eb · D.C.

in; Makes me want to shout, "Hal-le-lu-jah! I feel good!"___
go; Makes me want to shout, "Hal-le-lu-jah! I feel good!"___
face, I'm a gon-na shout, "Hal-le-lu-jah! I feel good!"___

The Steps Of A Good Man   78

Psalm 37:23
3 Part Round

Music by Don Marsh

I · Eb · Fm/Eb · Eb · Bb7 · Eb · II

The steps of a good man are or-dered by the Lord. The steps of a

Fm/Eb · Eb · Bb7 · Eb · III · Fm/Eb · Eb · Bb7 · Eb

good man are or-dered by the Lord. And he de-light-eth in His way.

The Blood Will Never Lose Its Power

Words & Music by
Andrae Crouch

1. The blood that Je-sus shed for me, Way back on
2. It soothes my doubts and calms my fears, And it dries

Cal - va - ry, The blood that gives me strength from day to
all my tears. The blood that gives me strength from day to

day, It will nev - er lose its pow'r. It

Chorus

reach - es to the high - est moun - tain, It

THE BLOOD WILL NEVER LOSE ITS POWER

flows_ to the low - est val - ley._____ The blood that gives me

strength from day__ to day, It will nev - er lose__ its pow'r._____

Nothing But The Blood

80

R.L.

Robert Lowry

Oh! pre - cious is the flow That makes me white as snow; —

No oth - er fount I know, Noth-ing but the blood of Je - sus.

He Looked Beyond My Fault

Words by Dottie Rambo

Music - Adapted from Londonderry Ai

A - maz - ing grace shall al - ways be my song of praise, For it was
grace that bought my lib - er - ty, I do not know just why He came to
love me so. He looked be - yond my fault and saw my need.

Refrain

I shall for - ev - er lift mine eyes to Cal - va - ry to view the

HE LOOKED BEYOND MY FAULT

Cross where Je - sus died for me,___ How mar-vel - ous the grace that caught my fall - ing soul. He looked be - yond my fault and saw_ my_ need.____

Glory To His Name

.B. Simpson

J.H. Burke

Glo - ry to His name,___ Glo - ry to_ His name,___ All may change,_ but Je - sus nev - er! Glo - ry to His name.____

Learning To Lean

Words & Music by
John Stallings

With a triplet feeling

Chorus

Learn - ing ___ to lean, learn - ing ___ to lean, I'm learn - ing to lean on Je - sus. Find - ing ___ more pow - er ___ than I'd ev - er dreamed, I'm learn - ing to lean on Je - sus.

Verse

1. The joy ___ I can't ex - plain ___ fills ___ my soul, since the
2. There's glo - ri - ous vic - t'ry each day now, for me, and ___

day I made Je-sus my King._____ His bless-ed Ho-ly Spir-it is
I found His peace so se-rene._____ He helps me with each task___ if

lead-ing my way; He's_ teach-ing and I'm learn-ing to lean._____
on-ly, I'll ask; Ev-'ry day now I am learn-ing to lean._____

Leaning On The Everlasting Arms 84

Rev. E.A. Hoffman

A.J. Showalter

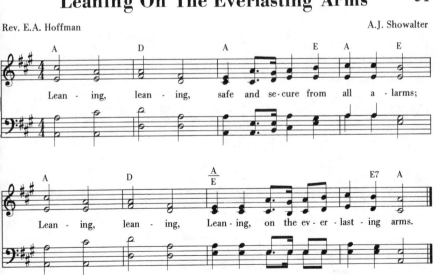

Lean-ing, lean-ing, safe and se-cure from all a-larms;

Lean-ing, lean-ing, Lean-ing, on the ev-er-last-ing arms.

All Because Of God's Amazing Grace

Words & Music by Stephen Adams

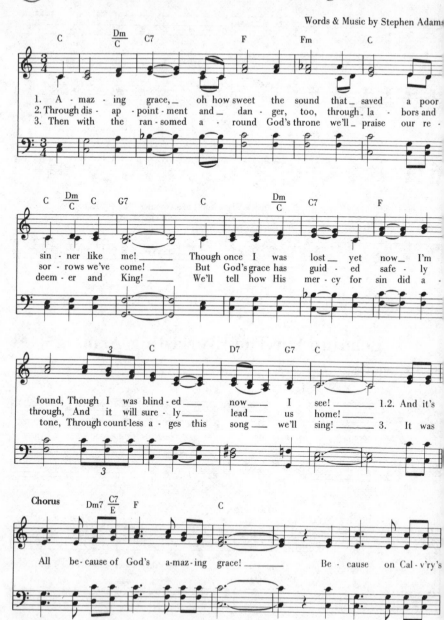

1. A - maz - ing grace, oh how sweet the sound that saved a poor
2. Through dis - ap - point - ment and dan - ger, too, through la - bors and
3. Then with the ran - somed a - round God's throne we'll praise our re -

sin - ner like me! Though once I was lost yet now I'm
sor - rows we've come! But God's grace has guid - ed safe - ly
deem - er and King! We'll tell how His mer - cy for sin did a -

found, Though I was blind - ed now I see! 1.2. And it's
through, And it will sure - ly lead us home! 3. It was
tone, Through count - less a - ges this song we'll sing!

Chorus

All be - cause of God's a - maz - ing grace! Be - cause on Cal - v'ry's

ALL BECAUSE OF GOD'S AMAZING GRACE

moun-tain He took my place! _____ And some-day, some glo-rious morn-ing _ I shall

see Him face to face, All be cause of God's a - maz - ing grace! _____

I Love Him

Traditional

I love Him, I love Him, Be - cause He first loved

me; And pur - chased my sal - va - tion on Cal - v'ry's tree.

Where The Spirit Of The Lord Is

Words & Music by
Stephen R. Adams

Where the Spir - it of the Lord is, There is peace, Where the Spir - it of the Lord is, There is love. There is com - fort in life's dark - est ho - ur there is light and life, there is help and pow-er in the Spir - it, in the Spir - it of the Lord.____

Jesus Is His Name

Words & Music by
W. Elmo Mercer

1. There is One who is with me— as I walk down life's high-way,— Je - sus—
2. When I cried out for mer - cy— there was One who brought par-don,— Je - sus—

is His— name;— On His arm I am lean-ing,— And on Him I'm de -pend-ing,—
is His— name;— When I fell in my weak-ness. There was One who re - stored me,—
D.S. There is one who's for - giv -ing— This I know, Hal-le -lu -jah! —

1 *To Refrain* **2** Refrain

Je - sus is His name.———— name.———
Je - sus is His name.———— name.——— One who is lov -ing,—
Je - sus is His name.———— name.———

One who is true; One who is watch-ing,— All that I do.

89 I Keep Falling In Love With Him

Words & Music by
Lanny Wolfe

1. When I first fell in love with Je - sus, I gave Him all my
2. There's a hand that I hold on to through each val - ley and each

heart, And I thought I could - n't love Him more than I
trial, There's a shoul - der that I lean up - on as I

did right at the start; But now I look back o - ver the moun -
face an - oth - er mile; And there's a love that I can de - pend

tains and the val - leys where I've been, And it makes me know I
on it's fresh and new each day, And with love my heart is

I KEEP FALLING IN LOVE WITH HIM

days go by,___ Oh what a love___ be -tween my

Gm6 D

Lord and I ___ just keep fall -ing in love ___ with Him

A7   Bb7   A7   G   D

o -ver and o - ver and o -ver and o - ver a - gain.

90

Jesus Made A Believer

Words & Music by
Lanny & Marietta Wolfe

Je - sus made a be - liev - er ___ out of

JESUS MADE A BELIEVER

91

I Shall Not Be Moved

Words by John T. Benson, Jr.

Music by Mrs. James A. Pate

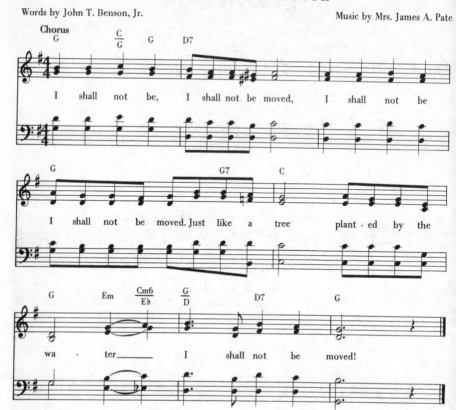

I shall not be, I shall not be moved, I shall not be I shall not be moved. Just like a tree plant-ed by the wa - ter I shall not be moved!

92

More About Jesus

E.E. Hewitt

Jno. R. Sweney

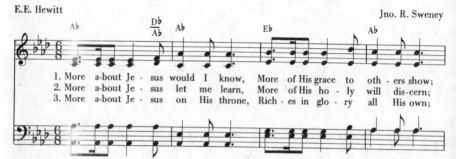

1. More a-bout Je - sus would I know, More of His grace to oth - ers show;
2. More a-bout Je - sus let me learn, More of His ho - ly will dis-cern;
3. More a-bout Je - sus on His throne, Rich - es in glo - ry all His own;

More of His sav - ing full - ness see, More of His love who died for me.
Spir - it of God, my teach - er be, Show - ing the things of Christ to me.
More of His king - dom's sure in - crease; More of His com - ing Prince of Peace.

D.S. — More of His sav - ing full-ness see, More of His love who died for me.

Refrain

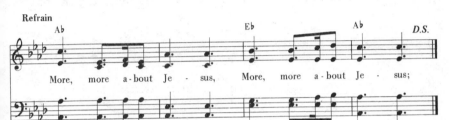

More, more a - bout Je - sus, More, more a - bout Je - sus;

The Name Of Jesus

93

Words by W. Martin

Music by E. Lorenz

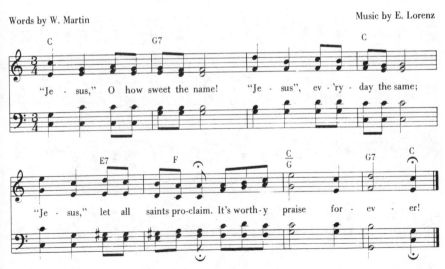

"Je - sus," O how sweet the name! "Je - sus", ev - 'ry - day the same;

"Je - sus," let all saints pro-claim. It's worth-y praise for - ev - er!

Let My Light Shine

Words & Music by
Dallas Holm

Chorus

Let my light shine in the night-time Let it shine all day through;

Let it shine shine for Je-sus May it shine

shine on you!

Verse

1. I was walk-ing a-long in the
2. Now I'm liv-ing for just one

dark-ness I did-n't know which way to go; Then the Lord,
pur-pose To let the Lord shine through me; If His love

He turned the light on, He changed my life and saved my soul.
can shine on oth-ers, Then His Spir-it can set them free.

I Want Jesus More Than Anything

Words & Music by
Don Marsh

I WANT JESUS MORE THAN ANYTHING

I WANT JESUS MORE THAN ANYTHING

The World Didn't Give It To Me

(and the world can't take it away)

Words & Music by
Gary S. Paxton
William J. & Gloria Gaither

THE WORLD DIDN'T GIVE IT TO ME

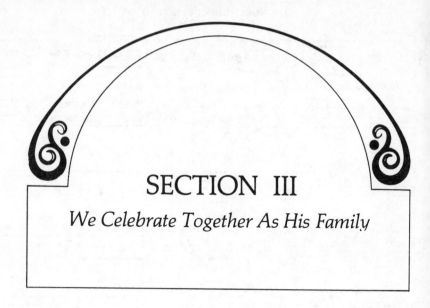

SECTION III

We Celebrate Together As His Family

97

God's Wonderful People

Words & Music by
Lanny Wolfe

I love the thrill that I feel when I get to-geth-er with, God's won-der-ful peo-ple, Love the

GOD'S WONDERFUL PEOPLE

God's Family

Words & Music by
Lanny Wolfe

1. We're part of the fam - 'ly that's been born a - gain;
2. When a broth - er meets sor - row we all feel His grief;
3. And tho' some go be - fore us, we'll all meet a - gain;

Part of the fam - 'ly whose love knows no end. For
passed through the val - ley we all feel re - lief. To -
in - side the ci - ty as we en - ter in. There'll

Je - sus has saved us, and made us His own. Now we're
geth - er in sun - shine, to - geth - er in rain, To -
be no part - ing, with Je - sus we'll be To -

part of the fam - 'ly that's on its way home. When he's
geth - er in vic - t'ry, thro' His pre - cious name. And
geth - er for ev - er, God's fam - i - ly. Just

GOD'S FAMILY

Chorus

some-times we laugh ___ to -geth-er, ___ Some-times we cry. ___

Some-times we share ___ to -geth-er ___ heart-aches and sighs. ___

Some-times we dream ___ to -geth-er ___ of how it will be ___

___ When we all get to Heav - en, God's fam-i - ly. ___

A Warm Family Feeling

Words & Music by
Jerry Nelson

1. All God's peo- ple share a feel- ing that this world can't un- der
2. There are folks who've joined this fam- 'ly; We don't e- ven know their

stand; When a broth- er's heart is bro- ken _____ and He
names. They might speak a dif- f'rent lan- guage ___ but we're a

needs a help- ing hand _____ right be- side him is an-
fam- 'ly just the same ___ we've been a- dopt- ed by the

oth- er Who will lis- ten to his cares; Who can
Fa- ther been ac- cept- ed by the Son; But the

A WARM FAMILY FEELING

sense the weight of sor - row, And can feel the pain he bears. There's a
thrill is still in know - ing, It's His blood that makes us one.

Chorus

warm fam - 'ly feel - ing in the pres - ence of the Lord. For we

share each oth - er's bur - dens, __ all our hearts in one ac - cord. There's a

bond that finds us kneel - ing where we feel the Spir - it's

heal - ing. What a warm fam - 'ly feel - ing, In the pres - ence of the Lord.

Someone Is Praying For You

100

Words & Music by
Lanny Wolfe

1. When it seems that you've prayed 'til your strength is all gone, And your
2. Have the clouds 'round you gath-ered in the midst of a storm, Is your

tears fall like rain - drops all the day long. Je - sus cares and He
ship tossed and bat - tered, are you wea - ry and worn? Don't lose hope some - one

knows just how much you can bear; He'll speak your name to
pray - ing for you this ver - y day; And "Peace be still" is al

some - one in prayer. Some - one is pray - ing for
read - y on the way.

Chorus

Some - one is pray - ing for

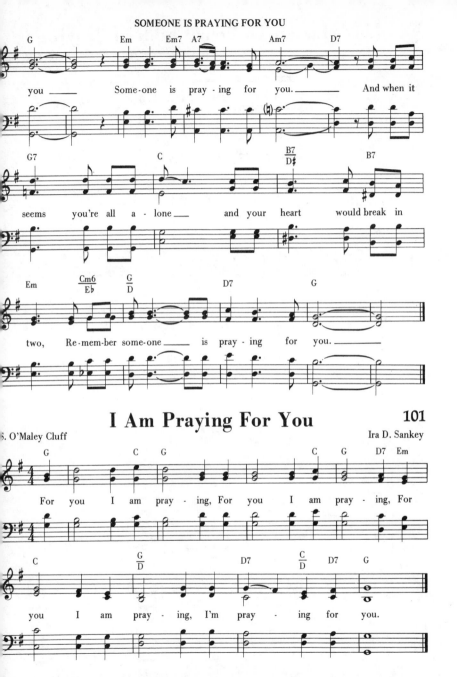

you _____ Some-one is pray-ing for you. _____ And when it

seems you're all a - lone ___ and your heart would break in

two, Re-mem-ber some-one _____ is pray-ing for you. _____

I Am Praying For You

101

S. O'Maley Cluff

Ira D. Sankey

For you I am pray - ing, For you I am pray - ing, For

you I am pray - ing, I'm pray - ing for you.

102 Lord, Listen To Your Children Praying

Words & Music by
Ken Medema

Lord, lis-ten to Your chil-dren pray-in';

Lord, send Your Spir-it in this place! Lord, lis-ten to Your chil-dren pray-in'; Send us love, send us pow'r, send us grace!

103 People

Brightly
Chorus

Words & Music by
Dony McGuire

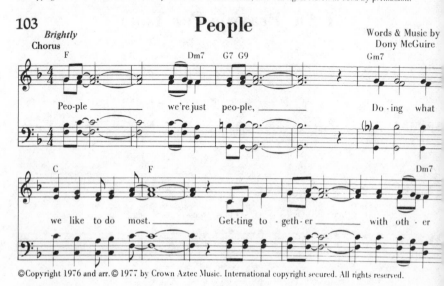

Peo-ple ___ we're just peo-ple, ___ Do-ing what

we like to do most. ___ Get-ting to-geth-er ___ with oth-er

PEOPLE

peo - ple, _____ Lift - in' our voic - es to the Lord! _____

Verse

1. We are ____ noth - ing spe - cial, But in a
2. Some - days for us at times get rough, _____ We

way ____ we're spe - cial too, ____ 'Cause you've come ____ here to
e - ven get the blues, ____ But when our ____ day comes

join us, _____ And to live we do need you! ____ 'Cause we're
to an end it's ____ been made good by you! ____

Follow Jesus

Words & Music by
Danny Lee

Fol-low Je - sus, I will fol-low Je - sus; An - y - where_ He

leads me I will fol - low, leads I'll go!_ A-cross the riv - er,

Down through the val - ley, Or if it be on the moun-tain high;_

I'll go, Lord, an - y-where You want. me; Take me, here am I. _____

Blest Be The Tie

hn Fawcett

Hans G. Nägeli

1. Blest be ___ the tie ___ that binds Our hearts ___ in
2. Be - fore ___ our Fa - ther's throne We pour ___ our
3. We share ___ our mu - tual woes, Our mu - tual
4. When we ___ a - sun - der part, It gives ___ us

Chris - tian love; The fel - low ship ___ of
ar - dent prayers; Our fears, ___ our hopes, ___ our
bur - dens bear; And oft - en for ___ each
in - ward pain; But we ___ shall still ___ be

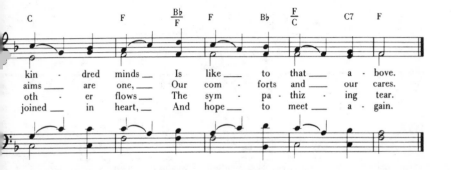

kin - dred minds ___ Is like ___ to that ___ a - bove.
aims ___ are one, ___ Our com - forts and ___ our cares.
oth - er flows ___ The sym - pa - thiz - ing tear.
joined ___ in heart, ___ And hope ___ to meet ___ a - gain.

Closer To You

Words & Music I
Don Marsh

1. Help me to know You as I once knew You, Help me to
2. Turn me from sin now I would be ho - ly, In true re

seek You as I once sought You; Help me to love You as I on
pen - tance I hum-bly come; ___ All that I am now and ev - e
D.S. love You as I on

loved You! ___ Bring me back close, Lord, clos - er to
will be, ___ I glad - ly sur - ren - der in - to Your
loved You, ___ Bring me back close, Lord, clos - er to

Chorus

Fine
You.
care.
You.
Clos - er to You, Lord, clos - er to You, for I have

wan - dered ___ so far from Your lov - ing voice. I want t

D.S. al Fin

Let Them Know

Words by Lanny & Marietta Wolfe

Music by Lanny Wolfe

Let them know, let them know, — Tell them Je - sus loves them

so; Loves them so much that to Cal-va - ry He would go; —

— Let them know Let them know — that they too can —

go To live for - ev - er-more with Je - sus, Let them know, — Let them know.

Surely The Presence Of The Lord
Is In This Place

Words & Music by
Lanny Wolfe

Sure - ly the pres - ence of the Lord is in this place, I can feel His might - y pow - er · and His grace. _____ I can hear the brush of an - gel's wings, I see glo - ry on each face; Sure - ly the pres - ence, of the Lord is in this place.

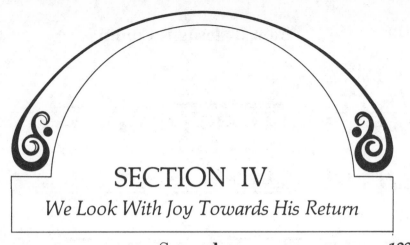

SECTION IV
We Look With Joy Towards His Return

Someday

(It May Be Tomorrow)

109

Words & Music by
Danny Lee

Some - day, there'll be no more sor - row, Some - day we'll

walk hand in hand; Some - day, it may be to - mor - row,

We'll walk to - geth - er through the prom - ised land.

Shout It, Jesus Is Coming

Words & Music by
Lanny Wolfe

Come on and shout it from the moun-tain top, __ Pro-claim it in the cit-y streets. __

Sing it ev -'ry-where you go, __ Tell ev- 'ry - bod-y you meet. Shout it!

Je -sus is com - ing, Je-sus is com -ing, Je-sus is com - ing, Yes, He's com - ing, let the

whole word know that Je-sus is com-ing soon! ver- y soon! Shout it! __

The Year When Jesus Comes

Words & Music by
Lanny Wolfe

1. What if this would be the year when Je - sus comes, _____
2. What if this would be the day when Je - sus comes, _____
3. What if this would be the mo - ment Je - sus comes, _____

____ The year that we've been wait - ing for so long? _____ We'd
____ The day that we've been wait - ing for so long? _____ We'd
____ The mo - ment we've been wait - ing for so long? _____ We'd

have so lit - tle time to get our lost world won, _____
have so lit - tle time to get our lost world won, _____
have no time, no time to get our lost world won, _____

____ If this would be the year when Je - sus comes! _____
____ If this would be the day when Je - sus comes! _____
____ If this would be the mo - ment Je - sus comes! _____

God's Forever Family

Words & Music by
Del Delamont

1. There's a move-ment stir-ring all a-cross the earth, And the un-i-verse pre-pares for His re-turn. As the chil-dren of the Lord a-wait the com-ing of that day our hearts are joined in love, and prayer. and praise! What a

2. We've all mourned the loss of loved ones and of friends, But the time will come we'll see them all a-gain. All the chil-dren of the sec-ond birth will meet a-round His throne, when God's for-ev-er fam-'ly gath-ers home!

3. Oh the priv-i-lege of meet-ing face to face, Out of ev-'ry kind-red, na-tion, tribe and race. All the mul-ti-tudes of rel-a-tives that we had nev-er known, when God's for-ev-er fam-'ly gath-ers home!

GOD'S FOREVER FAMILY

Chorus

grand and glo - rious meet-ing, when we hear the Sav - ior greet-ing, All the

saints that He has ran - somed for His own. _____ And we shall

join in praise for - ev - er in that great e - ter - nal

song, When God's for - ev - er fam - 'ly gath - ers home! _____

With Gladness And Joy

113

Words & Music by
Rich Cook

Even eighths

1. The tri - als and the heart-aches will soon be wiped a-
2. The lame, the blind, the crip - pled He touched up - on the
3. The pear - ly gates are o - pened, The gold - en streets are

way, the dan - gers of this life will soon be past. ___ A
earth, a - wait ___ to ___ look up - on His face. ___ On
lined with Saints of God who've won the vic - to - ry. ___ The

day of hope is com - ing, a ___ day when we can
earth they felt His pres - ence as they gath - ered in His
trum - pet blasts are sound - ing, the ___ choir be - gins to

sing to ___ Je - sus and ___ hail Him as our King! It's with
name, and ___ now they bow and sing, "A - maz - ing Grace!" ___ It's with
sing, Here comes Je - sus the ___ King of all ___ Kings! ___

WITH GLADNESS AND JOY

Chorus

glad - ness ___ and joy we come ___ be - fore the King, With ___

glad - ness ___ and joy the courts ___ of Heav - en ring. I can

hear ___ the glad ho - san - nas ___ they're shout - ing;"King of

Kings;"It's with glad - ness ___ and joy we come ___ be - fore the King!

It's About Time For His Coming

Words & Music by
Don Marsh

1. It's a-bout time for His com-ing, It's a-bout time for His com-ing, It's a-bout time for the com-ing,_____ The com-ing of ___ the Lord. It's a-bout time for His com-ing, It's a-bout time for His com-ing, It's a-bout

2. It's a-bout time are you read-y? It's a-bout time are you read-y? It's a-bout time are you read-y?_____ For the com-ing of ___ the Lord. It's a-bout time are you read-y? It's a-bout time are you read-y? It's a-bout

3. It's a-bout time yes I'm read-y, It's a-bout time yes I'm read-y, It's a-bout time yes I'm read-y,_____ For the com-ing of ___ the Lord. It's a-bout time yes I'm read-y, It's a-bout time yes I'm read-y, It's a-bout

* Other suggested verses, "It's about time, let us praise Him! etc." "It's about time, Hallelujah! etc."

time   for His com - ing, _____   The_   com - ing   of _ the   Lord!
time   are you read - y? _____   For the   com - ing   of _ the   Lord!
time   yes I'm read - y, _____   for the   com - ing   of _ the   Lord!

I Am Bound For The Promised Land   115

Samuel Stennett   Traditional

1. On_ Jor - dan's storm - y   banks I   stand,_ And   cast a   wish - ful   eye
2. When_ shall I   reach_ that   hap - py   place,_ And   be for - ev - er   blest?

To_ Ca - naan's_ fair and   hap - py   land, Where_ my   pos - ses - sions   lie.
When_ shall I _ see   my   Fa - ther's face, And_ in   His_ bos - om   rest?

D.S. – O   who will   come and   go with me? I am bound for the prom-ised land.

Refrain

I am bound for the prom-ised   land,....   I am bound for the prom - ised   land;

116 We'll Understand It Better

F   Bb   F   G7   C7   F

By and by when the morn-ing comes; When the saints of God are gath-ered home, We will

Bb   F   C7   F

tell the sto - ry how we've ov - er-come: For we'll un-der-stand it bet-ter by and by.

117 Soon And Very Soon

Words & Music by
Andrae Crouch

F   Bb/F   F

1. Soon and ver - y soon _ we are goin' to see the King, _
2. No more cry - in' there _ we are goin' to see the King, _
3. No more dy - in' there _ we are goin' to see the King, _
4. Soon and ver - y soon _ we are goin' to see the King, _

C7   F

Soon and ver - y soon _ we are goin' to see the King, _
No more cry - in' there _ we are goin' to see the King, _
No more dy - in' there _ we are goin' to see the King, _
Soon and ver - y soon _ we are goin' to see the King, _

SOON AND VERY SOON

Soon and ver - y soon ___ we are goin' to see the King, ___
No more cry - in' there ___ we are goin' to see the King, ___
No more dy - in' there ___ we are goin' to see the King, ___
Soon and ver - y soon ___ we are goin' to see the King, ___

___ Hal - le - lu - jah, ___ Hal - le - lu - jah, ___ we're

goin' to see the King! ___ ___ Hal - le - lu - ia, Hal - le -

lu - jah, Hal - le - lu - jah, Hal - le - lu - jah.

118

Are You Ready?

Will L. Thompson

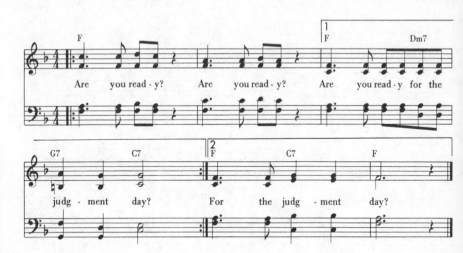

Are you read-y? Are you read-y? Are you read-y for the
judg-ment day? For the judg-ment day?

119

I'll Be Leavin'

Words & Music by Terry Harper

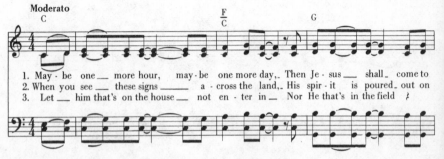

1. May-be one __ more hour, may-be one more day, Then Je-sus __ shall __ come to
2. When you see __ these signs _____ a-cross the land, His spir-it is poured __ out on
3. Let __ him that's on the house __ not en-ter in __ Nor He that's in the field

I'LL BE LEAVIN'

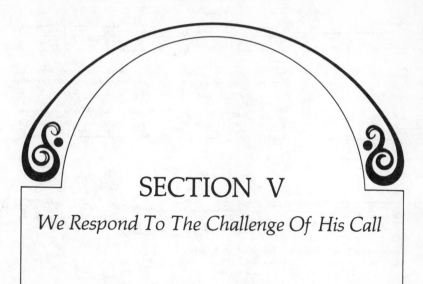

SECTION V

We Respond To The Challenge Of His Call

120

Jesus Is Everything

Words & Music by
Don Marsh

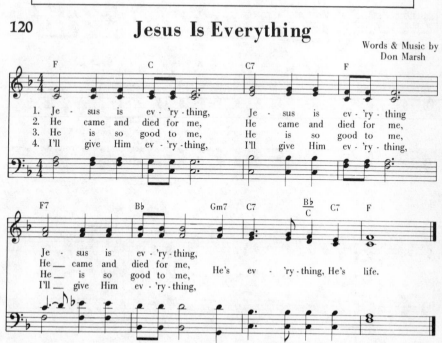

1. Je - sus is ev - 'ry - thing, Je - sus is ev - 'ry - thing
2. He came and died for me, He came and died for me,
3. He is so good to me, He is so good to me,
4. I'll give Him ev - 'ry - thing, I'll give Him ev - 'ry - thing,

Je - sus is ev - 'ry - thing,
He __ came and died for me, He's ev - 'ry - thing, He's life.
He __ is so good to me,
I'll __ give Him ev - 'ry - thing,

Flow Through Me

Words & Music by
Tim Sheppard

Flow through me, Pour through me. Riv - ers of mer - cy and

foun - tains of bless - ing. Let me see more of Thee,

Filled with Thy pow - er and love. _____

Chorus

Al - le - lu - ia, Al - le - lu - ia.

I Wish You All Could Know Him

Words & Music by
Phil Johnson

I wish you all would love Him like I love Him

I wish you all could see Him like I do, like I do!

I wish you all could feel His sweet presence

I wish you all could know Him like I know Him!

Come Unto Jesus

Words & Music by
Dallas Holm

Chorus

Come un - to Je - sus, Give Him your life to - day.

Come un - to Je - sus, Let Him have His way.

Verse

1. Oh I know there are things in your life, You think He can't for-give;
2. Don't put it___ off my___ friend, You can't af - ford to wait;

But He'll for-give and for - get, my friend, and show you how to live.
To - day___ is the___ day for you, soon it will be too late.

Only One Life

Words & Music by
Lanny Wolfe

1. It __ mat - ters so lit - tle how much you may own, The
2. You may take all the trea - sures from far a - way lands; __
3. The days pass so swift - ly, the months come and go, The

plac - es you've been __ or the peo - ple you've known. For it
Take all the rich - es you can hold in your hands; And __
years melt a - way __ like new fal - len snow; __

all comes to noth - ing when placed at His feet, It's
take all the plea - sures your mon - ey can buy, But
Spring turns to sum - mer and sum - mer to fall, __

noth - ing to Je - sus, Just __ mem - 'ries to keep.
what will you have __ when it's your time to die.
Au - tumn brings win - ter, then __ death comes to call.

ONLY ONE LIFE

Chorus

On - ly one life, so soon it will pass; On - ly what's done for Christ will__ last! On - ly one chance to do His will; so give to Je - sus all your days, It's the on - ly life that pays when you re - call you have but one life!__

Lord, I Need You

Words & Music by
Terry Harper

Take my life, take my soul, cleanse my heart and make me whole. Touch my eyes and let me see the count-less things that You do for me. And when I bow on my knees and pray, to make You Mas-ter of ev-'ry day, that ev-'ry breath I breathe may say, "Lord I need _____ You."

Holy Spirit, Flow Through Me

126

Words & Music by
Walt Mills

1. Ho - ly Spir - it, _____ Flow through me, _____ Ho - ly
2. Ho - ly Spir - it, _____ Rest on me, _____ Ho - ly
3. Ho - ly Spir - it, ___ Flow out from me, _____ Ho - ly

Spir - it, _____ Flow through me, _____ And make my life _____ what it
Spir - it, _____ Rest on me, _____ And use me Lord to win the
Spir - it, _____ Flow out from me, _____ That oth - ers Lord ___ may see

ought to be, _____ Ho - ly Spir - it, ___ Flow through me.
lost to Thee, _____ Ho - ly Spir - it, ___ Rest on me.
you in me, _____ Ho - ly Spir - it, Flow out from me. _____

Give Them All To Jesus

Words by Bob Benson Sr. and Phil Johnson

Music by Phil Johnson

1. Are you tired of chas-ing pret-ty rain-bows?
2. He nev-er said you'd on-ly see sun-shine,

Are you tired of spin-ning 'round and 'round?
He nev-er said there'd be no rain;

Wrap up all the shat-tered dreams of your life,
He on-ly prom-ised a heart full of sing-ing,

And at the feet of Je-sus, lay them down.
A-bout the ver-y things that once brought pain.

Give them

GIVE THEM ALL TO JESUS

all,   give them   all;   Give them all __ to Je - sus;   Shat-tered

dreams, wound-ed   hearts, __   and bro-ken   toys. _____   Give them

all,   give them   all,   Give them all ___ to   Je -

- sus;   And   He   will turn. your sor - row,   in-to   joy! _____

If That Isn't Love

Words & Music by
Dottie Rambo

1. He left the splen-dor of Heav-en, Know-ing His des-ti
2. E-ven in death He re-mem-bered The thief hang-ing by His

ny was the lone-ly hill of Gol-go-tha, There to lay down His
side. He spoke with love and com-pas-sion, Then He took Him to

Chorus

life for me. If that is-n't love, the o-cean is dry,
Par-a-dise. then heav-en's a myth

There're no stars in the sky, And the spar-row can't fly! If
There's no feel-ing like this, If that is-n't love!

Music by Dottie Rambo and David Huntsinger

Words by Dottie Rambo

Jesus Be The Lord Of All

Words & Music by
Lanny & Marietta Wolfe

1. Je - sus be   the Lord   of all,   Je - sus be   the Lord   of all,
2. Je - sus, I   sur - ren - der all, Je - sus, I   sur - ren - der all,

Je - sus be   the Lord   of all   the king - doms of   my heart,
Je - sus, I   sur - ren - der all   the king - doms of   my heart.

Whatever It Takes

Words by Lanny & Marietta Wolfe

Music by Lanny Wolfe

What - ev - er _____ it takes   to draw clos - er   to

You Lord,_   That's what I'll be   will - ing   to   do; _____   For what-

WHATEVER IT TAKES

ev - er it takes to be more like You, That's what I'll be

will - ing to do._____ I'll trade sun-shine for rain, com-fort for

pain, That's what I'll be will - ing to do._____ For what - ev - er it

takes for my will to break; That's what I'll be will - ing to do._____

How Long Will You Wait?

Words & Music by
Jon A. Sherberg

friend You'll nev - er find the an - swer there. 'Til you make Je - sus your Lord and

D.C. al Fine

Mas - ter, all your search - ing will nev - er get you an - y - where.

My Jesus, I Love Thee

133

Words & Music by
Rich Cook

1. My Je - sus, I love Thee, My Je - sus, I love Thee, My
2. My Je - sus, I praise Thee, My Je - sus, I praise Thee, My
3. My Je - sus, I'll serve Thee, My Je - sus, I'll serve Thee, My

Je - sus, I love Thee, I love Thee, I do.
Je - sus, I praise Thee, I praise Thee, I do.
Je - sus, I'll serve Thee, I'll serve Thee, I will.

I'm Gonna Keep On Singin'

Words & Music by
Andrae Crouch

Chorus

1. I'm gon-na keep on sing - in', ___
2. I'm gon-na keep on march - in', ___
3. You trum-pets keep on sound - in', ___
4. I'm gon-na keep on sing - in', ___

I'm gon-na keep on shout - in', ___
I'm gon-na keep on fight - in', ___
You bells ___ keep on ring - in', ___
I'm gon-na keep on shout - in', ___

I'm gon-na keep on ___ lift - in' my voice ___ and let the
I'm gon-na keep on ___ lift - in' my voice ___ and let the
And ev-'ry bod-y keep lift - in' your voice ___ and let the
I'm gon-na keep on ___ lift - in' my voice ___ and let the

I'M GONNA KEEP ON SINGIN'

135

Take Our Love

Words & Music by
Derric Johnson

Your__ home.__ Take it all, Lord, make it Yours.

Take Me Back

136

Words & Music by
Andrae Crouch

Take me back, Take me back dear Lord, to the place where I first re-ceived You,

Take me back, Take me back, dear Lord where I first be-lieved!

Looking Through His Eyes

Words & Music by
Mike Otto

1. Let me see this world, dear Lord, as____ though I were
2. Let me see this world, dear Lord, through Your eyes when men

look - ing through Your eyes. ____ A ____ world ____ of men who don't
mock Your Ho - ly Name. ____ When they beat You and spat up -

want You, Lord, But a world ____ for ____ which ____ You ____ died.
on You, Lord, Let me love them as You loved them just the same. ____

Let me kneel ____ with You ____ in the gar - den ____ blur my
Let me stand high a - bove my pet - ty prob - lems, ____ and grieve for

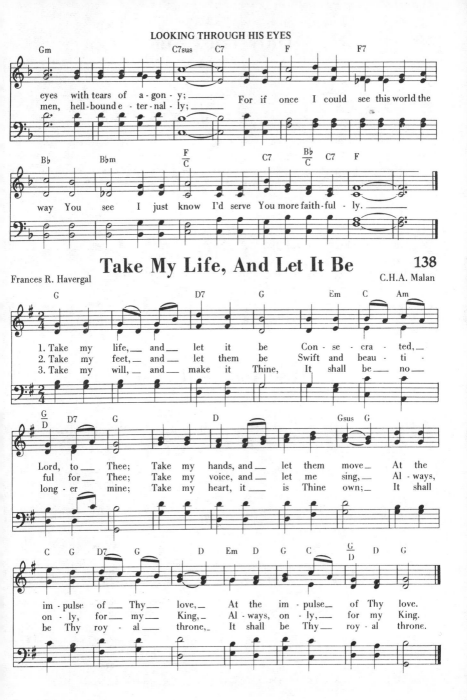

LOOKING THROUGH HIS EYES

Gm   C7sus   C7   F   F7

eyes with tears of a - gon - y; _____ For if once I could see this world the
men, hell - bound e - ter - nal - ly; _____

Bb   Bbm   F/C   C7   Bb/C   C7   F

way You see I just know I'd serve You more faith - ful - ly. _____

Take My Life, And Let It Be 138

Frances R. Havergal   C.H.A. Malan

G   D7   G   Em   C   Am

1. Take my life, _ and _ let it be Con - se - cra - ted, _
2. Take my feet, _ and _ let them be Swift and beau - ti -
3. Take my will, _ and _ make it Thine, It shall be _ no -

G/D   D7   G   D   Gsus   G

Lord, to _ Thee; Take my hands, and _ let them move _ At the
ful for _ Thee; Take my voice, and _ let me sing, _ Al - ways,
long - er mine; Take my heart, it _ is Thine own; _ It shall

C   G   D7   G   D   Em   D   G   C   G/D   D   G

im - pulse of _ Thy _ love, _ At the im - pulse _ of Thy love.
on - ly, for _ my _ King, Al - ways, on - ly, _ for my King.
be Thy roy - al _ throne, _ It shall be Thy _ roy - al throne.

Only Trust Him

J.H. Stockton

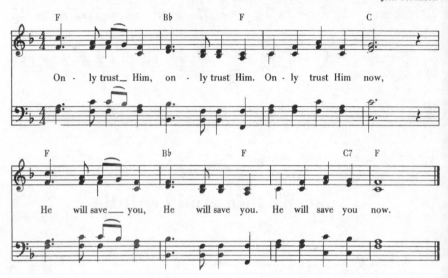

On - ly trust__ Him, on - ly trust Him. On - ly trust Him now,

He will save___ you, He will save you. He will save you now.

Rise And Be Healed

Words & Music by
Milton Bourgeois

1. Has fear and doubt come a - gainst__ your__ mind? Has your faith been
2. If by__ faith you__ reach out to__ Him, He will meet your

sore - ly tried?_____ Lift up your eyes here - com - eth your
ev - 'ry need._____ He will re - spond to the cry of your

RISE AND BE HEALED

If I Had It To Do All Over Again

Words & Music by
Dallas Holm

1. If I had it to do__ all o-ver a-gain, __ I'd serve
2. If you're look-ing for life, __ stop look-ing right now, __ for it's

Je - sus ev - 'ry day of my life, __ For I've found He a - lone__ can
Je - sus that can give life to you, __ So just o - pen your heart__ and

real - ly sat - is - fy and de - liv - er me from all sin and strife..
un - lock it's__ door, and let Je - sus cleanse your life through and through

Chorus

__ Yes it's Je - sus, the on - ly one__

Je - sus, God's on - ly Son,__ Yes, it's Je - sus, that

set my soul free,__ and it's Je - sus Christ that's com-ing back for me.

I'll Live For Him

142

Words by R. Hudson

■ Music by C. Dunbar

1. My life, my love I give to Thee, Thou Lamb of God who died for me;
2. O Thou who died on Cal - va - ry, To save my soul and make me free,

Chorus — I'll live for Him who died for me, How hap - py then my life shall be!

Oh may I ev - er faith-ful be, My Sav - ior and my God!
I'll con - se-crate my life to Thee, My Sav - ior and my God!
I'll live for Him who died for me, My Sav - ior and my God!

143

Jesus

(He Means All The World To Me)

Words & Music by
Lanny Wolfe

Je - sus, Je - sus, He means all ___ the world to me. ___ Je - sus, Je - sus, Je - sus, With - out Him where would I be?

144

I Love You, Jesus

Words & Music by
Stephen Adams

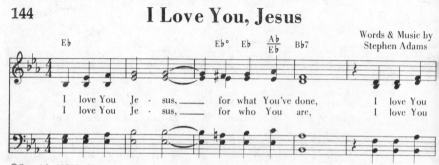

I love You Je - sus, ___ for what You've done, I love You
I love You Je - sus, ___ for who You are, I love You

I LOVE YOU, JESUS

Je - sus ____ for what You've done. You've giv - en life to me, ____
Je - sus ____ for who You are. You are the Son of God, ____

____ You've set my spir - it free; I love You, Je - sus, for what You've done. ____
____ My re - sur - rec - ted Lord; I love You, Je - sus, for who You are. ____

I Surrender All

145

J.W. Van DeVenter

W.S. Weeden

I sur - ren - der all, I sur - ren - der all;

All to Thee, my bless - ed Sav - iour, I sur - ren - der all.

Bring All Your Needs To The Altar

Words & Music by
Dottie Rambo

1. Walk bold - ly to stand in His pres - ence, _____ Lay claim to the prom - ise He made. _____ Your soul can be cleansed 'neath the flow of the foun - tain, His blood wash - es guilt all a - way. _____

2. He watch - es the fall of the spar - row, _____ Con - cerned with the lil - ies so fair. _____ How much more He cares for the sheep of His pas - ture, So bring Him your bur - dens to bear. _____

Chorus

Bring all your needs to the al - tar, _____ Bring all your

Just As I Am

147

Charlotte Elliott

William B. Bradbury

1. Just as I am, with-out one plea, But that Thy blood was shed for me,
2. Just as I am, and wait-ing not To rid my soul of one dark blot,
3. Just as I am, though tossed a-bout With many a con flict, many a doubt,
4. Just as I am Thou wilt re-ceive, Wilt wel-come par-don, cleanse, re-lieve,

And that Thou bidd'st me come to Thee, O Lamb of God, I come! I come!
To Thee whose blood can cleanse each spot, O Lamb of God, I come! I come!
Fight-ings and fears with-in, with-out, O Lamb of God, I come! I come!
Be-cause Thy prom-ise I be-lieve, O Lamb of God, I come! I come!

My Faith Still Holds

Words by William J. & Gloria Gaither

Music by William J. Gaither

My faith still holds on to the Christ of Cal-va-ry,

Oh bless-ed Rock of A-ges, cleft for me.

I glad-ly place my trust in things I can-not see,

My faith still holds on to the Christ of Cal-va-ry!

Is There Anything I Can Do For You? 149

Words & Music by
Dottie Rambo and David Huntsinger

1. Is there an-y-thing I can do for You? An-y-thing I can do? For all the things You've done for me, Is there an-y-thing I can do?
2. Is there an-y-thing I can be for You? An-y-thing I can be? For all the things You've been to me, Is there an-y-thing I can be? I'm
3. Is there an-y-where I can go for You? An-y-where I can go? For sak - ing all to fol - low Thee, Is there an-y-where I can go?

will - ing to be used, dear Lord, What - e'er the price may be. So if there's

an-y-thing I can be for You, Just make it known to me.
(an -y-where) go

TOPICAL INDEX: